**A**

▶▶ KEY POINTS ▶▶

▶ All living things share the following living processes: ~~...~~
sensitivity, excretion, respiration, nutrition and repr...

1 Unscramble the names of the following living processes:

tevemomn   tudoponercir   nertcieox   wotrgh

....

seytvinitsi   tornitnui   pitaniroser

....   *[2 marks]*

2 Tick the boxes below which contain processes common to all living things.

| swimming | talking | moving |

| flowering | feeding | flying |

[4 marks]

3 Explain what is meant by **nutrition**.

....

....

[2 marks]

4 Explain why animals need to move.

....

....

[1 mark]

5 Name the process by which a plant creates a new young plant.

....

[1 mark]

KEY POINTS

- Animals and plants can be grouped together by the things they have in common, such as a backbone, wings or flowers.
- Each classification group has a special name and particular characteristics.
- Plants and animals with similar characteristics can be sorted into groups using a key.

1 Identify the following animals using this branch diagram:

A

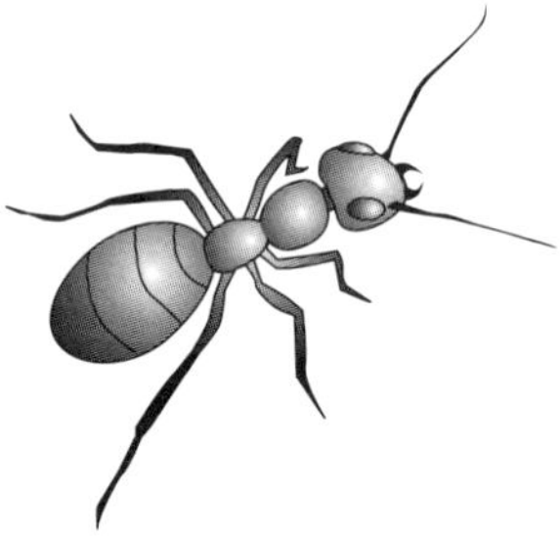

B

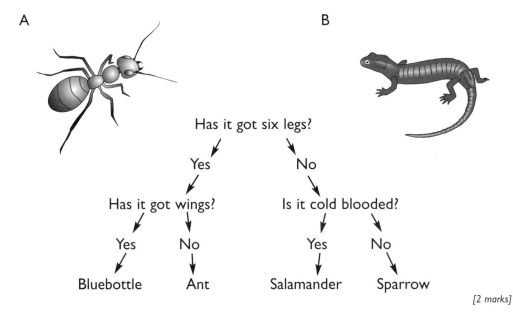

Has it got six legs?
- Yes → Has it got wings?
  - Yes → Bluebottle
  - No → Ant
- No → Is it cold blooded?
  - Yes → Salamander
  - No → Sparrow

[2 marks]

2 Identify these plants using the branch diagram on the next page:

A

B

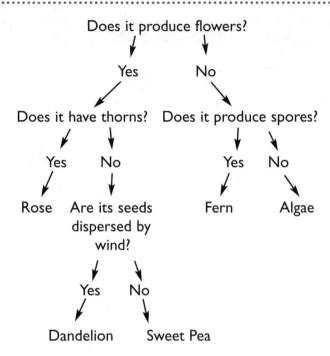

Does it produce flowers?

Yes — Does it have thorns?

No — Does it produce spores?

Does it have thorns?
Yes — Rose
No — Are its seeds dispersed by wind?

Does it produce spores?
Yes — Fern
No — Algae

Are its seeds dispersed by wind?
Yes — Dandelion
No — Sweet Pea

[2 marks]

3 Join the animals on the left to their correct classification group. (Some of the groups may have more than one animal joined to them.)

frog   fish

polar bear   amphibians

penguin   reptiles

grass snake   birds

dolphin   mammals

owl

shark

[2 marks]

▶▶ KEY POINTS ▶▶

- ▶ The sepal protects the brightly coloured and scented petals.
- ▶ The male part of a plant is the stamen, made up of the anther, which produces pollen, and the filament.
- ▶ The female part of the plant is the carpel, made up of the stigma, style and ovary (this ripens into the fruit).
- ▶ Pollen is transferred from the stamen to the stigma and fertilizes egg cells in the ovary to produce seeds. Pollen is carried by:
  - (a) Wind - pollen is blown from one flower to another.
  - (b) Insects - pollen rubs off on insects visiting flowers and is carried to other flowers.
- ▶ Seeds are dispersed by:
  - (a) Wind - wind blows some types of seed over long distances (eg a dandelion clock).
  - (b) Animals - birds and animals eat the fruit of flowering plants and the undigested seeds pass through their systems.
  - (c) Explosion - pods containing seeds explode and eject the seeds (eg sweet pea).

1   Complete the labels on this diagram of a flowering plant:

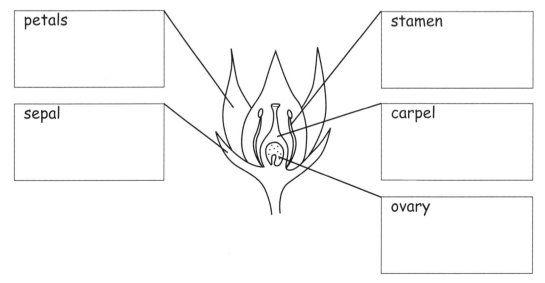

petals

stamen

sepal

carpel

ovary

[5 marks]

▶▶ KEY POINTS ▶▶

▶ A plant needs air, light, heat, nutrients and water to grow well.
▶ Photosynthesis is the way in which a plant takes carbon dioxide from the air, and with water and light creates sugar for food.
▶ If a plant is deprived of light it will turn yellow and eventually die.
▶ The roots of a plant take up water and nutrients from the soil and also anchor the plant.
▶ Plants grow faster in warm countries and more slowly in cold countries.

1 Name the conditions needed for healthy plant growth.

....
....
[2 marks]

2 (a) Explain why light is essential for a plant to grow.

....
....
[1 mark]

(b) Describe what would happen if a plant did not have light.

....
....
[1 mark]

3 What **two** purposes do the roots have in a flowering plant?

....
....
[2 marks]

4 A group of children tried the following experiment on a football pitch. They covered half the pitch with a large black plastic sheet and the other half with a large clear plastic sheet.

After four weeks both sheets were taken off the pitch.
In the boxes below, write what you think the grass would look like and why.

Black Plastic Sheet

Clear Plastic Sheet

[2 marks]

5 Why do you think plants stop growing in the winter?

....
....
[1 mark]

5

▶▶ **KEY** POINTS ▶▶

- ▶ Habitat means a place where a plant or animal lives.
- ▶ Habitats may be large or small, eg desert or garden pond.
- ▶ Animals and plants are suited to live in their habitats, and would not be suited to live in all environments.

1 Match each of these animals and plants with its correct habitat.

hermit crab	desert
worm	near a pond
cactus	seashore
frog	under a stone
woodlouse	in soil

[2 marks]

2 Explain how each of the plants and animals is suited to live in its habitat.

(a) Owl

....
[1 mark]

(b) Polar bear

....
[1 mark]

(c) Salmon

....
[1 mark]

3 Why is the desert **not a good habitat** for a polar bear? List as many reasons as you can.

....

....
[2 marks]

4 Why is a pond a **good habitat** for a frog? List as many reasons as you can.

....

.... *[2 marks]*

▶▶ KEY POINTS ▶▶

▶ Most food chains start with a green plant; when food chains are linked, they are called a food web.
▶ All plants are producers because they make their own food.
▶ All animals are consumers because they eat other plants and animals.
▶ A predator is an animal which gets its food by eating other animals.
▶ Prey are the animals that predators eat.
▶ An animal or plant can be part of more than one food chain.

1 Look at this food chain.

cabbage ⟶ **snail** ⟶ **blackbird** ⟶ **kestrel**

(a) Which is the producer?   (b) Which are the consumers?

....

(c) Which are the predators?   (d) What are their prey?

....
                                                                                  [4 marks]

2 Look at this food web:

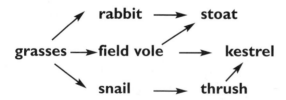

(a) What would be the effect on the food web if there were less grass than usual one year?

....

....
                                                                                  [2 marks]

(b) What would be the effect on the food web if there were more kestrels born than usual one year?

....

.... *[2 marks]*   **7**

▶▶ KEY POINTS ▶▶

▶ The four main food groups are:
   (a) carbohydrates - give the body energy
                     - found in cereals, potatoes, bread, pasta, sugar
   (b) proteins   - build up the body and aid in cell repair
                   - found in fish, meat, eggs, dairy produce, lentils, nuts
   (c) fats   - give the body a lot of energy
                   - found in butter, cheese, sausages, bacon
   (d) vitamins and - help the body to grow and stay healthy
       minerals   - build bones and teeth and help muscles work
                   - found in fruit, vegetables, fish, meat, cheese
▶ A healthy diet contains foods from all these groups in the right amounts.
▶ Smoking is bad for your health because the tar in cigarettes damages the lungs. Nicotine is the drug found in cigarettes that makes them addictive. Smoking near other people can cause them harm.
▶ Too much alcohol damages the liver and brain and slows your reactions.
▶ Some other drugs can be harmful.

1   Name the **four** main food groups:

   ....

   ....

   ....

   ....
   [2 marks]

2   Choose one of the food groups and state why the body needs it.

   ....

   ....

   ....
   [1 mark]

3   This is today's menu for the school canteen. Do you think today's choices offer a balanced diet? Give your reasons.

Fish fingers
Chips
Sausage Sandwich
Doughnuts
Chocolate cake

   ....

   ....
   [2 marks]

4   Why is smoking bad for your health?

   ....

   ....
   [1 mark]

5   Why is it never safe to drive a car after drinking alcohol?

   ....

   ....
   [2 marks]

▶▶ KEY POINTS ▶▶

▶ The heart is a powerful muscle which pumps blood around the body.
▶ Blood circulates around the body through arteries, veins and capillaries.
▶ Veins carry blood back to the heart; arteries carry blood away from the heart; capillaries are small blood vessels which allow gas in and out of the blood.
▶ Through respiration (breathing) oxygen is taken into the blood and carbon dioxide is removed from it.
▶ Pulse is a measurement of heart rate. Exercise makes the pulse faster .
▶ Regular exercise and healthy eating help to keep the circulatory system healthy.
▶ Smoking, lack of exercise and fatty foods can lead to an unhealthy circulatory system.

1 Tick the boxes that contain good advice for a healthy heart. Put a cross in the boxes that contain things that are bad for your heart.

regular exercise	fatty foods	smoking	fruit and vegetables

[1 mark]

(a) For one of the boxes you have ticked, explain why this is good for your heart.

....

....
[1 mark]

(b) For one of the boxes you have crossed, explain why this is bad for your heart.

....

....
[1 mark]

2 Explain the difference between veins and arteries.

....

....

continued on next page>

3 Helen was interested to know how her heart rate changed after doing different activities. After each activity she rested and measured her heart rate at three different times. Her results are shown in the table below.

Activity	Heart rate (beats per minute)		
	Just after activity	2 minutes after activity	15 minutes after activity
Resting	70	70	70
Working at desk	72	72	71
Slow jogging	125	100	72
Running	171	115	71

(a) Explain why Helen's heart rate stayed the same when she had only been resting.

....

....

[1 mark]

(b) Explain why Helen's heart rate was higher when she was jogging and running.

....

....

[1 mark]

(c) What do you notice about Helen's heart rate 15 minutes after each activity.

....

....

[1 mark]

▶▶ KEY POINTS ▶▶

▶ Babies do not need teeth as they only drink milk and eat soft foods.

▶ Children grow a set of 20 milk teeth.

▶ Adults develop a set of 32 permanent teeth.

▶ The three types of teeth are:
Incisors - used for cutting food
Canines - used for cutting and tearing food
Molars - used for grinding and chewing food.

▶ Sugar in food attracts bacteria in the mouth and produces plaque on teeth.
Plaque produces an acid that attacks tooth enamel causing decay.

▶ Decay can be prevented by:
Brushing teeth properly twice a day
Regular visits to the dentist
Avoiding foods containing too much sugar.

1 Label the diagram below:

name:
purpose:

name:
purpose:

name:
purpose:

[1 mark]

2 Simon goes to bed and forgets to brush his teeth. When he wakes up he notices a white slimy layer on his teeth.

(a) What is this layer called?

....

[1 mark]

(b) Describe how it has been formed

....

....[2 marks]

(c) Other than regularly brushing his teeth, give three more ways in which Simon can look after his teeth.

(i) ....

....

(ii) ....

....

(iii) ....

....

[2 marks]

▶▶ **KEY** **POINTS** ▶▶

▶ The skeleton has three main functions:
   (a) Protects vital organs, eg skull/brain, rib cage/heart and lungs.
   (b) Supports body when standing, sitting etc.
   (c) Allows movement, eg walking, running and throwing.
▶ Bones are joined in three main ways:
   (a) Hinge joints, eg elbow and knee.
   (b) Ball and socket joints, eg hip and shoulder.
   (c) Sliding (plain) joints, eg wrist and ankle.
   Cartilage protects the ends of the bones, and allows them to move easily.
▶ Tendons attach muscles to bones, and ligaments attach bones to bones.
▶ Bones are made of calcium.
▶ Muscles usually work in pairs, eg triceps and biceps. Muscles are attached to bones by tendons and move bones by contracting and relaxing. Muscles can only pull, they cannot push.

1   Write down **three** different ways in which having a skeleton is important to us.

....

....

....

[3 marks]

2 (a) What is a joint?

....

[1 mark]

(b) Name three types of joints and give an example of each.

....

....

....

[3 marks]

3 Complete the following paragraph by putting in the missing words:

Muscles pull _____ by contracting and _____ .
Muscles usually work in _____. Muscles are attached to bones by
_____. Muscles can only _____ , they cannot _____.

[2 marks]

>> **KEY** POINTS >>

▸ An egg is fertilized by a sperm and grows into an embryo. The embryo develops into a baby, which is born after nine months.
▸ The baby develops and grows into a child.
▸ Puberty is when a child's body develops into an adult's body.
▸ Adults are able to reproduce and continue the life cycle.

1 Complete the missing words in the diagram of the human life cycle.

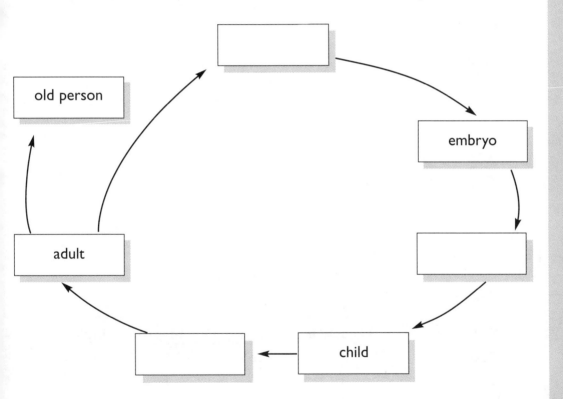

[1 mark]

►► KEY POINTS ►►

▶ Some materials, eg rock, wood and cotton, are natural.
▶ Some materials are man-made, eg nylon, plastic and glass.
▶ Materials have properties (special features) which make them useful for different jobs, eg glass is transparent, so it is a good material for windows.
▶ Materials may be combined (mixed together) to make new materials.

1 Sort these materials out into two groups - natural and man-made - and write the names in the circles.

cotton   oil   petrol   nylon   stone   iron   silk   plastic   wood   glass

natural   **man-made**

[2 marks]

2 Look at this chart. Ameena has been testing the properties of materials to see which materials would be good for making an umbrella.
Here are her results:

Material	Transparent	Strong	Waterproof	Light
Cotton	✗	✔	✗	✔
Clear Polythene	✔	✔	✔	✔
Tissue paper	✗	✗	✗	✔
Kitchen foil	✗	✔	✔	✔
Perspex	✔	✔	✔	✔

(a) Which materials were both transparent and waterproof?

....
[1 mark]

(b) Why would cotton not be a good material to use for an umbrella?

....
[1 mark]

(c) Which material might Ameena have thought was best for an umbrella, and why?

....
[2 marks]

3 Look at this picture of a house and see which materials it is made from. Why do you think the builder chose each of these materials to make the house? Give as much detail as you can.

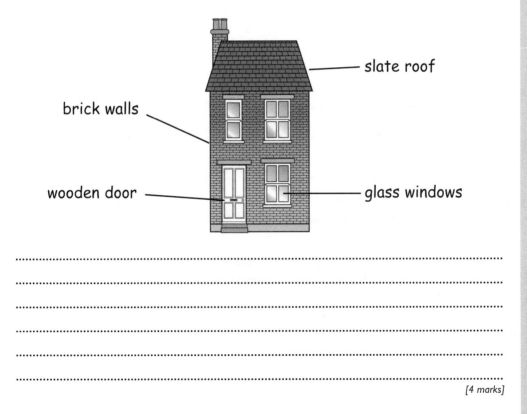

slate roof

brick walls

wooden door

glass windows

....
....
....
....
....
....
[4 marks]

▶▶ KEY POINTS ▶▶

▶ All materials can be classified as being a solid, a liquid or a gas.

▶ Solids can be held; solids have a definite shape and can keep this shape; solids can be cut or shaped.

▶ Liquids flow downwards; liquids take up the shape of the container they are in; they find their own level; they may be poured; they are not easy to hold.

▶ Gases are usually invisible; they fill up empty spaces; a mixture of gases, in the form of air, is all around us.

▶ If we heat a solid, we may be able to change it into a liquid or a gas. If we cool a gas, we may be able to change it into a liquid or a solid, eg ice, water and water vapour.

1 (a) I can move freely; I am hard to contain.

What am I? ....

(b) I keep my shape and may be held.

What am I? ....

(c) My surface stays level in a container and I may be poured.

What am I?...

[3 marks]

2 Water can change its state from a solid to a liquid to a gas. Fill in this diagram to show the changes in state of the water:

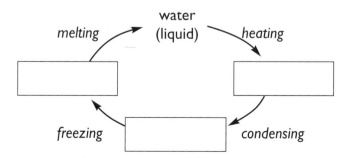

[2 marks]

3 Explain what these everyday objects are made of in terms of solids, liquids and gases.

A
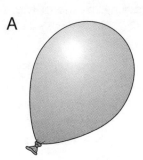

B

The outside of object A is a ....

The inside of object A is a ....

I know this because

....

....

[2 marks]

The outside of object B is a ....

The inside of object B is a ....

I know this because

....

....

[2 marks]

What will be inside bottle B once some of the tomato sauce has been used?

....

....

[1 mark]

▶▶ KEY POINTS ▶▶

▸ Materials can be changed by heating and cooling. Some of these changes can be reversed and some cannot.

▸ Melting a solid turns it into a liquid.

▸ Evaporating a liquid turns it into a gas.

▸ Condensing a gas turns it into a liquid.

▸ Freezing a liquid turns it into a solid.

▸ Melting, evaporating, condensing and freezing are reversible changes.

▸ Cooking and burning change materials completely. These changes are irreversible; the materials cannot be changed back.

1 Describe, with an example, what is meant by a **reversible** change.

....

....

[2 marks]

2 Describe, with an example, what is meant by an **irreversible** change.

....

....

[2 marks]

3 A saucer of water is left on a windowsill above a warm radiator. After a few days there appears to be less water in the saucer.
Explain why this has happened. What is this process called?

....

....

[2 marks]

4 Sanjay breathes on a window.
Describe what he would see. What is this process called?

....

....

[2 marks]

▶▶ KEY POINTS ▶▶

▶ Water vapour evaporates from the sea, rivers and lakes as the sun heats it.
▶ As the water vapour rises it cools and condenses to form clouds.
▶ The clouds cool and water droplets are formed.
▶ The water droplets fall as rain back into the sea, rivers and lakes.
▶ These four stages make up the water cycle.

1 Complete the boxes in as much detail as you can:

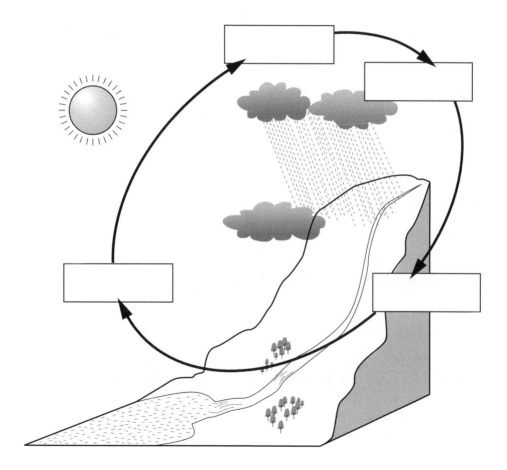

[4 marks]

▶▶ **KEY** POINTS ▶▶

- A mixture made up of solid particles, eg sand and pebbles, may be separated by sieving.
- Solid particles mixed with a liquid, eg. sand in water, can be separated by filtering.
- Some solids can dissolve in water or other liquids to make a solution, eg salt and sugar; they can be separated by evaporation.
- There is a limit to the amount of solids which can dissolve into a given amount of liquid. When a liquid can't dissolve any more solid matter, it is called a saturated solution.
- Iron and steel may be separated from a mixture of solid materials using magnets.

1 Megan has been trying to dissolve some chalk in water. The chalk does not dissolve. What would be the quickest way for Megan to separate the chalk from the water?

....

[1 mark]

2 Jim has to sort out the recycling bank, but someone has mixed aluminium cans with steel cans. How could Jim separate the aluminium and steel cans?

....

[1 mark]

3 Gary and Steven have a container of pasta shapes and rice which have been mixed together by accident. How could they separate the two ingredients?

....

....

[1 mark]

4 Shaheen has separated a mixture of pebbles, sand, salt and water.
The salt had been dissolved in the water, and the pebbles and the sand were lying at the bottom of the container.
Number the processes below in the order that Shaheen would have used them to separate her mixture.

☐   ☐   ☐

filtering   evaporation   sieving

    [2 marks]

►► KEY POINTS ►►

▶ Some materials let heat pass through them easily; these materials are called thermal conductors.

▶ Some materials do not let heat pass through them as easily; these materials are called thermal insulators.

▶ Heat will travel from a warmer area to a cooler one.

▶ Some materials let electricity flow through them easily; these materials are called electrical conductors.

▶ Some materials do not allow electricity to flow through them; these materials are called electrical insulators.

▶ Conductors can complete a circuit, but insulators can't; metals conduct electricity, most non-metals don't.

1 Seema and Steven have been testing the electrical conductivity of different materials by making them part of an electrical circuit. Decide whether the bulb will light up when each of the test materials in turn is placed in the circuit. Tick the boxes for those that conduct electricity.

Battery

Bulb

Test Material

Test materials:

plastic spoon ☐
kitchen foil ☐
metal fork ☐
piece of string ☐

[2 marks]

2 Why is a saucepan made of metal, yet the handle is often wood or plastic?

....

[2 marks]

3 Why do we wear thick coats and jumpers when the weather is cold?

....

[1 mark]

4 Why are the wires in a plug made of copper, yet the outside of the plug and the flex are made of plastic?

.... *[2 marks]*

▶▶ KEY POINTS ▶▶

- ▶ Rocks and soils are natural materials.
- ▶ Rocks can be organized according to their hardness.
- ▶ Some rocks let water through (permeable) and some don't (impermeable).
- ▶ Soils are made of tiny bits of rock, dead plants and minibeasts, air and water.
- ▶ Some soils are better at letting water drain through than others.

I Some children have been investigating rocks. They have put their information into the chart below. Look carefully at it and answer the questions:

Rocks	Scratched by: Fingernail	2p coin	Steel nail	Lets water through
Granite	✘	✘	✘	✘
Sandstone	✘	✔	✔	✔
Flint	✘	✘	✘	✘
Chalk	✔	✔	✔	✔

(a) Which rocks are permeable?

....
[1 mark]

(b) Name one rock that is harder than sandstone.

....
[1 mark]

2 Look at the pictures of three soil samples.

(1) sandy   (2) clay   (3) pebbles

(a) Which soil sample would let water through most quickly? Explain.

....

....

....
[2 marks]

(b) Which soil sample is the least permeable?

....
[1 mark]

▶▶ KEY POINTS ▶▶

▶ Sources of light include light bulbs, candles, torches, the sun and stars.
▶ Light travels in straight lines and bounces off objects.
▶ We can see light sources and objects because the light from them travels to and enters our eyes.
▶ Shiny objects such as mirrors and metal reflect light well. Dark, dull objects do not reflect light well.
▶ Light bounces off a mirror at the same angle as it hits it.

1 Light comes from various sources.
   Tick each of the light sources:

   mirror   ☐   candle   ☐

   switched-on TV set ☐   the sun ☐

   the earth   ☐   torch   ☐

   [3 marks]

2 Shane lights a candle in the living room and places a mirror in the doorway between the living room and the kitchen, as shown in the plan diagram below.

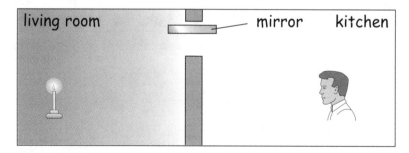

   Draw two arrows to show how Shane can see the candle when he is standing in the kitchen.

   [2 marks]

3 Why can you see yourself when you look at a polished metal tray?

   ....

   ....

   [1 mark]

▶▶ **KEY** POINTS ▶▶

- ▶ Light cannot travel through solid (opaque) objects.
- ▶ When an object blocks out the light a shadow is formed.
- ▶ Some objects allow light to pass through them; they are transparent.
- ▶ The sun is our light source and casts shadows.
- ▶ The sun appears to move across the sky during the day although it is actually the earth that moves.
- ▶ The sun affects the length of shadows during the day; these are shortest at midday and longest at the beginning and end of the day.

1   Helen stands in the playground on a bright, sunny day and notices her shadow on the ground. How is this shadow formed?

....

[2 marks]

2   Look at the following diagram:

9am	11am	noon	2pm

(a) What happens to the shadow as the sun appears to move across the sky?

....

[1 mark]

(b) At what time of day is a shadow at its shortest?

....

[1 mark]

3   Why does an empty milk bottle not cast a dark shadow?

....

[1 mark]

4   Simon shines a light through various objects onto a piece of white board. Tick the objects that you think will form a shadow.

clear plastic bottle ☐   jam jar ☐   book ☐

lens of a magnifying glass ☐   sieve ☐   wooden ruler ☐

[3 marks]

▶▶ **KEY** POINTS ▶▶

▶ The sun, moon and earth are almost spherical.
▶ The earth travels around the sun.
▶ The earth is kept in orbit (travelling around) by the sun's gravitational pull.
▶ It takes 365 days for the earth to orbit the sun.
▶ As the earth orbits the sun it rotates on its tilted axis causing day and night.
▶ The moon orbits the earth once every 28 days.

1 How long does the moon take to orbit the earth?

....
[1 mark]

2 Fill in the missing labels on the diagram.

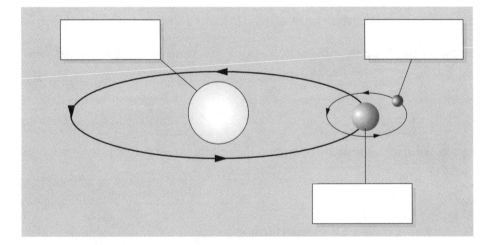

[1 mark]

3 The earth spins on its axis as it orbits the sun, causing day and night.
What do you think would happen if the earth stopped spinning?

....

....
[1 mark]

4 How many times does the earth spin on its axis during one orbit of the sun?

....
[1 mark]

▶▶ KEY POINTS ▶▶

- ▶ Friction is a force that tries to stop things sliding against each other.
- ▶ Friction produces heat.
- ▶ Friction slows things down quickly on rough surfaces like roads, but not as quickly on smoother surfaces like ice.
- ▶ Air resistance, or drag, tries to slow you down when you are moving, eg riding a bike, doing the long jump or running. Drag also slows you down in water when you swim.

1 Rest the palm of your hand lightly on the table and try to move it over the table top; it should move quite easy. Now press down on your hand and try to move it; it will be much harder to move, because the force of friction gets bigger as the force pushing the surfaces together gets greater.
Now put a sheet of paper between your hand and the desk.

Describe what happens now when you try to push your hand across the table. Explain why this happens.

....

....

[2 marks]

2 Why do we use a smooth substance like oil in car engines?

....

....

[1 mark]

3 Explain what is meant by **streamlining**.

....

....

[2 marks]

4 Why are the blades on ice skates narrow and sharp?

....

....

[1 mark]

5 Why are the soles of trainers rough and bumpy?

....

.... *[1 mark]*

▸▸ **KEY** POINTS ▸▸

- ▸ All forces are either pushes or pulls.
- ▸ Gravity is the downward pull of the earth towards its centre.
- ▸ Mass is the amount of matter (stuff) that makes up an object.

1 The cat knocks over the plant pot.

(a) What is the name of the force that makes the plant pot fall to the ground?

....

[1 mark]

(b) Explain what is meant by the term **gravity**.

....

....

....

[1 mark]

2 Some children have been experimenting with force meters. They have measured a range of objects using the force meter and have put their results into a table:

Object	Force meter reading in Newtons
Scissors	4.5
Cup	5.0
Toy car	2.0
Keys	3.5

(a) Which object produced the most force?

.... *[1 mark]*

(b) How do you know this?

....

....

....

[1 mark]

3 Write a statement that links the weight of an object to the amount of stretch on the spring in a force meter.

....

....

....

[2 marks]

▶▶ **KEY** POINTS ▶▶

▶ Upthrust is the upward push on an object in water.
▶ If the upthrust on an object is equal to the pull down from gravity then an object will float.
▶ If gravity is greater than upthrust, the object will sink.

I Look at this toy boat floating on the pond. The air is still.

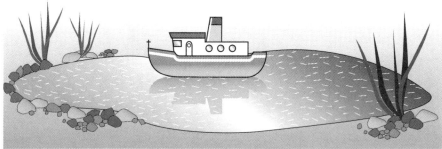

(a) Which two forces are acting on the boat?

....

[2 marks]

(b) What do you know about the forces acting on the boat if the boat is floating?

....

....

[1 mark]

(c) Show the size and direction of the forces acting on the boat using arrows on the diagram above.

[1 mark]

Jack loaded the boat up with blocks and the boat sank.

(d) What has happened to the forces acting on the boat?

....

....

....

....

[1 mark]

▶▶ **KEY POINTS** ▶▶

▸ When forces acting on an object are balanced, an object at rest stays still.
▸ Unbalanced forces make things speed up, slow down, or change direction.
▸ Arrows are used in diagrams to show the directions and sizes of forces. For example, gravity always pulls down, so arrows to indicate gravity point downwards. The size of the arrow indicates the size of the force. When forces are balanced, the arrows are of an equal size; if one force was bigger, the arrow indicating it would also be bigger.

1 These drawings show balanced forces.

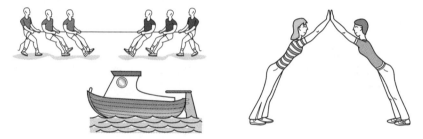

Use arrows to show the direction and size of the forces acting on these objects.

[3 marks]

2 Here is a ball at rest. It is about to be kicked by the foot on the left.

(a) Describe what will happen to the ball when it is kicked and after it has been kicked? Try to use the terms **force**, **balanced** and **unbalanced** in your answer.

....

....

[3 marks]

(b) Which force brings it back down to earth again?

.... *[1 mark]*   **29**

▶▶ **KEY** POINTS ▶▶

- ▶ Magnets have two poles: north and south .
- ▶ If you try to put two magnets together with the same poles touching, eg north and north, the magnets will repel each other (push away from each other).
- ▶ If you try to put two magnets together with different poles touching, eg north and south, they will attract (move towards each other).
- ▶ Magnets can exert a force of attraction on some materials, such as iron and steel; these materials are magnetic. (Not all metals are magnetic, however.)
- ▶ Magnets have a magnetic field; this is the area around them in which their magnetic attraction works.
- ▶ The magnetic attraction of a magnet is stronger at its poles and weaker towards the centre.

1 Look at these pairs of magnets.
Write **attract** or **repel** next to each pair, according to whether they will attract or repel each other.

| S | N | | N | S | | N | S | | N | S | | N | S | | S | N |

(a) . . . .   (b) . . . .   (c) . . . .

[3 marks]

2 Stephanie is working on an experiment to see which materials are attracted to magnets. Complete the chart she is using to record her results.

Material	Magnetic	Non- magnetic
Iron nail Plastic spoon Aluminium foil Wooden peg Steel paper clips New 2p coin	✔	✗

[3 marks]

3 Fill in the missing words:

Magnets have two poles, a _____ and a _____ . Magnets will pick up things made of _____ and _____ . If a magnet attracts an object, we say that the object is _____ . Magnets are strongest at their _____ and weaker in the _____ .

[2 marks]

▶▶ **KEY** POINTS ▶▶

▶ Some electrical devices use electricity from the mains (cooker, hairdryer); some smaller electrical devices use electricity from batteries (calculator, torch).

▶ Wire correctly connected to a battery will allow electricity to flow through it.

▶ Electricity can only travel in one direction.

▶ A switch added to a circuit can be used to break the flow of electricity.

▶ Adding more batteries to a circuit or shortening the wires in it will make a bulb shine brighter.

▶ These symbols are used to draw circuits:

battery	bulb	motor	switch (off)	switch (on)
—⊣⊢—	—⊗—	—Ⓜ—	—∘⟋∘—	—∘ ∘—

1 Andy has a battery, switch, bulb and some wire. He wants to make a circuit which will light the bulb and allow him to switch it on and off. Draw a diagram, using the correct symbols, to show a circuit which would work.

[2 marks]

2 Say what a switch is used for in a circuit.

....

....

[1 marks]

3 Steven has made a circuit to run a small electric motor and light a bulb. Although the bulb lights up, the motor does not work. A picture of Steven's circuit is shown below:

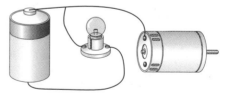

Why does is not work?

....

....

[1 mark]

4 The power supplied from a battery to a bulb makes two things happen to the bulb. What are they?

....

....

[2 marks]

31

- All sound is caused by vibration.
- No noise occurs when a sound source ceases to vibrate.
- Not all vibrations can be seen.
- Pitch (how high or low a sound is) and loudness can be changed.
- We hear sounds when vibrations from a sound source reach our ears through the air.
- Sound can travel through different materials. It travels better through some materials than others.

I   Look at the bottles. If you tapped each in turn, which one would have

(a) The lowest-pitched sound?   ....

(b) The highest-pitched sound?   ....

[2 marks]

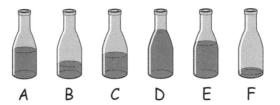

A   B   C   D   E   F

2   Gary and Narinder hit a cymbal and let it vibrate.

(a) When do you think the sound would be loudest: as soon as they hit the cymbal or after 2 seconds?

....

[1 mark]

(b) What would the sound be like after 5 seconds: **louder** or a **little quieter** or **the same volume**?

.... *[1 mark]*

(c) After 20 seconds, they couldn't hear any more sound. Can you explain what has happened to the cymbal? How do you know?

....

.... *[2 marks]*